SAM SILVER: U[...]

DEAD MAN'S HAND

Collect all the Sam Silver: Undercover Pirate *books*

DEAD MAN'S HAND

Jan Burchett and Sara Vogler

Illustrated by Leo Hartas

Orion
Children's Books

First published in Great Britain in 2013
by Orion Children's Books
a division of the Orion Publishing Group Ltd
Orion House
5 Upper St Martin's Lane
London WC2H 9EA
An Hachette UK company

The Orion Publishing Group's policy is to use papers that are
natural, renewable and recyclable products and made from wood grown
in sustainable forests. The logging and manufacturing processes are expected
to conform to the environmental regulations of the country of origin.

A catalogue record for this book is available from the British Library.

Printed in Great Britain by Clays Ltd, St Ives plc

For Captain Amber,
our editor and shipmate, arrgh!

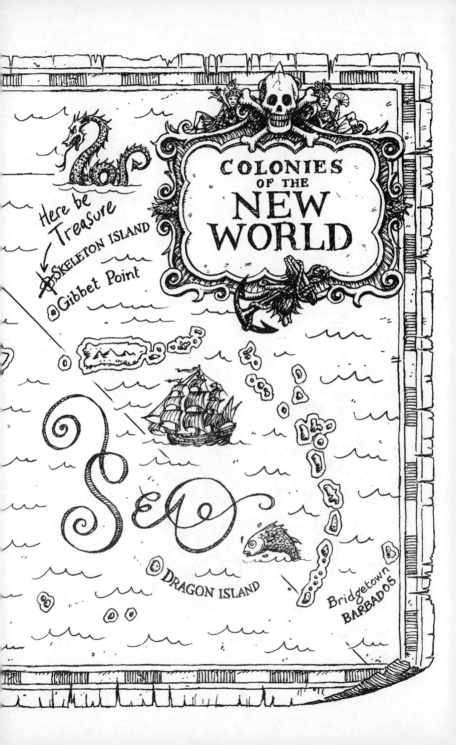

Here be Treasure

SKELETON ISLAND

Gibbet Point

COLONIES
OF THE
NEW
WORLD

Sea

DRAGON ISLAND

Bridgetown
BARBADOS

The SEA WOLF

Captain's Cabin
Hammocks
Gun Deck
Galley
Ship's Stores

CHAPTER ONE

S am Silver clung to the rigging of the
Sea Wolf. He could hear the frightened
shouts of his crewmates below. The
blinding rain lashed down and a vicious
wind ripped his clothes. Sam looked out
at the churning sea. Wave after wave
was breaking over the ship's rail, sending
foam far into the air and making the ship
lurch dangerously. Suddenly a wall of

grey water blocked everything from his view. It towered over him, higher than the tallest mast. The crew cried out in terror and, with a horrific cracking sound, the ship smashed in two. Before Sam knew what was happening he was torn from the rigging by the force of the water and found himself tumbling headlong into the sea. Down, down he fell, sinking through the swirling ocean, struggling helplessly to push his way back to the surface. He was going to drown . . . he needed air . . . he had to take a breath . . .

Sam woke with a start, gulping hard. He

sat up and looked round wildly. He could breathe! He wasn't at the bottom of the ocean. He was in his own bedroom. The *Sea Wolf* hadn't sunk and his pirate friends weren't lost after all. It had all been a horrible dream.

But what if his nightmare had been a warning of some kind? He'd been on board the ship in many storms and he knew how dangerous they could be. He needed to know if Captain Blade and the crew were safe – and he couldn't phone them. There was only one way to find out. Sam turned on his light, took down the dirty old bottle that he kept on his shelf and tipped out the precious gold doubloon inside.

No one else knew the secret of Sam's gold coin. It had the power to whisk him back three hundred years in time to join Captain Blade and his bold crew on board the *Sea Wolf* – the best pirate ship that had ever sailed the Caribbean Sea.

Sam hastily threw on the old jeans, T-shirt and trainers that he always wore when he went pirating. He spat on the coin and rubbed it on his sleeve.

At once his tangled sheets, his pillow and his crumpled pyjamas whizzed around him as if he'd been caught in a giant vacuum cleaner. He closed his eyes and felt himself being lifted into the air. In the next instant, he landed in a heap on something hard. He opened his eyes quickly and found he was in the ship's storeroom that he knew so well. The floor was rocking gently. He couldn't hear any crashing waves or howling wind. The *Sea Wolf* hadn't been sunk.

But the horror of the dream was still lingering in his head. The ship might seem fine but he had to make sure that all his shipmates were OK. He ran over to a barrel where a pirate jerkin, neckerchief, belt and spyglass lay waiting for him. His friend Charlie always put them there, ready for his return. She was the only girl on the crew and the only one who knew he came from the twenty-first century. He couldn't tell the rest of the crew. They'd think he was mad.

Sam ran out of the storeroom and bounded up the steps towards the deck. Just before he reached the top, he stopped, dazzled by the bright sunlight. The sails billowed against the blue sky as the wind sent the ship scudding across the waves. Happy voices reached his ears and Sinbad the surly ship's cat was asleep on a coil of rope. He opened one evil eye and hissed at Sam. Sam crept past, giving him a wide berth. Sinbad was the fiercest member of the crew and nobody could go near him except for Charlie. If Sinbad was being his usual self then everything must be all right.

Sam leapt onto the main deck where
the pirates were crouched round sacks
and chests piled high on the wooden
boards. Captain Blade was standing in the
middle of his men. He wore red braids in
his beard and two belts full of fearsome
weapons across his chest.

"By the heavens, it's Sam Silver!" he
boomed as Sam ran towards him.

The pirates got to their feet, grinning. A boy, his wild curly hair tied in a bandana, leapt on Sam and gave him a hearty punch on the arm.

"My frrriend!" he exclaimed in delight. Fernando's Spanish accent always got stronger when he was excited.

Ned the bosun gazed out over the empty sea, looking puzzled. "Well I'll be a barracuda in a basket," he said. "How did you get here, Sam? There's no vessel in sight and I'm certain you didn't swim."

"Maybe he was dropped by an albatross!" laughed Ben Hudson.

Sam's brain buzzed as he tried to think of a way he could have reached the *Sea Wolf*. They wouldn't be laughing if he told them the truth!

"He must have stowed away on a passing ship," said Charlie, coming to his rescue as usual.

"Charlie's right," Sam added quickly. "It

was . . . a fishing boat. And you can't see her now because she's gone. When the *Sea Wolf* came into sight I jumped overboard in a barrel, paddled hard and here I am!"

"You're a true Silver!" declared the captain. "Your grandfather would have been proud of your wily ways."

All the crew but Charlie believed that Sam was the grandson of Joseph Silver, a heroic pirate, long-since dead. Sam went along with this. It was almost true. Joseph Silver had been his great-great-lots-of-greats-grandad, and it was Joseph's gold doubloon that brought Sam back to 1706. When Sam went home to the present, they all believed that he'd gone to help his poor widowed mother on her farm.

"Sam has Silver's luck too," said Ben.

"Aye, and a pirate's nose," agreed Harry Hopp, the first mate. "He can smell a treasure haul from a hundred miles!" He led Sam to the pile of sacks and chests,

his wooden leg thumping on the deck.
"You're just in time to help us sort our
plunder!"

CHAPTER TWO

"Brilliant," said Sam. "Where did the treasure come from?"

"We took it from the *Master of the Ocean*," said Captain Blade. "Titus Reynard's ship."

"Who's he?" asked Sam.

Oops, he thought at once. *The crew are all looking at me. This is someone I'm meant to know.*

"Sorry, I must have seaweed in my ears," he

said, giving them a rub. "Who did you say again?"

"You know Titus Reynard, Sam," said Charlie, fixing him with her eyes. "The rich merchant from Puerto Rico. He took over all that land on the eastern tip of the island and built the grandest house you ever saw. You must have heard of him. He's the biggest villain around these parts."

"Of course I have," said Sam nodding vigorously. "Big villain, lots of land. Who hasn't heard of him?"

"I wish Titus had been on board when we attacked," said Ben. "I'd have enjoyed seeing that cur watch his treasure disappear!"

"Luckily that lily-livered brother of his was there to entertain us," laughed Ned. "He kept leaping about and shouting, though none of his men took any notice."

"I warrant his crew would've fought

harder if Titus had been on board himself," said Captain Blade. "All his servants live in fear of him."

"Servants?" spat Peter the ship's cook. "Slaves more like, the way he treats them."

"Aye, none last long under his harsh rule," agreed Ned.

"Didn't they even try to follow you to get his treasure back?" asked Sam in surprise.

Fernando fingered the blade of his knife. "We told them what would happen to them if they did!"

"And we slashed their sails — just in case they changed their minds," added Charlie.

"Belay this talk!" ordered the captain. "Get the booty out for all to see."

"Pieces of eight!" came a loud squawk and a green parrot landed on Sam's head.

"Hello, Crow," Sam said in delight, coaxing him onto his shoulder. He began to open one of the sacks while the parrot chattered in his ear.

Captain Blade gulped and backed away to the rail.

The *Sea Wolf* captain could face the most fearsome sea monster and not turn a hair but the sight of Sam's feathery friend had him quivering in his shoes. Peter the cook said it was because a parrot had poked its beak up his nose when he was a baby, but all the crew had a different story to tell.

Since Blade so disliked parrots, everyone just pretended that Crow was a brightly coloured Caribbean crow. It was the only way that Blade would let him stay on board.

The crew dived on the sacks and chests, cutting them open and thrusting their hands inside to pull out the treasure.

"Well, boil my brains in a bucket!" exclaimed Ned, throwing a cheap metal goblet to the deck. "There's nothing of worth here!"

"Aye," agreed Harry Hopp, holding up a string of gaudy beads. "These are just glass."

"Perhaps that's where his wealth comes from," called Captain Blade. "He buys rubbish but tricks people into paying a lot for it."

"Yet Reynard's brother was shouting about 'the last piece of the puzzle' and 'the key to untold wealth'," said Charlie in surprise, "and he said he had to get it to Titus or his life wouldn't be worth living."

Fernando shrugged. "Just words to try to make the crew obey him. There's no key here . . ."

". . . and not enough wealth to buy more than a tot of rum in a tavern!" said Ben in disgust.

"Search again, men!" ordered Blade. "We might have missed something."

Muttering, the pirates began to pick gloomily through the piles of tin plates and cheap jewellery. Sam found a dirty wooden box under a sack. "Maybe there's something in here," he said hopefully. "No one's opened it yet."

"Having seen the rest of the cargo, it'll probably be someone's false teeth!" laughed Fernando.

Sam threw open the lid. Inside was a lumpy shape wrapped in an oilcloth. As he picked it up, the cloth fell away. Sam leapt back in alarm.

Something fell from his hands and clattered to the deck.

It was a skeletal hand.

CHAPTER THREE

Crow gave a squawk of fright and flapped off up to the top of the mast. The crew gathered round. Everyone fell silent as they gazed at the gruesome find. The hand lay on the deck, its long gnarled fingers curled tightly round a strange golden ball.

"It's horrible!" whispered Charlie. "It seems almost alive."

"What's it holding?" asked Sam, stepping towards it. "It looks valuable."

"Don't touch that thing!" warned Harry, pulling him back. "It's probably cursed!"

"Silver's luck will guard us against misfortune," said the captain. "Have a look, Sam."

Sam bent over the curious object and gave it a poke. They heard a sharp crack and the hand fell open, two of its fingers hanging broken at the knuckles. The ball rolled slowly over the deck. Sam picked it up.

"What could it be?" asked Fernando eagerly.

"I don't know," answered Sam, puzzled. The ball sparkled in the sun as he turned it round. "It's got jewels embedded in it and numbers and symbols engraved all over the surface."

"That'll be witchy writing!" said Harry. "We should throw it overboard!"

"Let me have a look," said Captain Blade. Sam handed him the ball. "This is no witch's tool," he told the crew. "I know exactly what it is. It's part of an astrolabe!"

"Of course!" exclaimed Peter. Peter was usually a gloomy pirate but now he sounded so excited that everyone stared at him in disbelief.

"An astrolabe?" asked Sam.

"Never heard of it," said Fernando. "Have you, Charlie?"

Charlie shook her head.

"An astrolabe is an instrument for working out where you are by looking at the stars," Peter told them.

"They're not used much any more," added Harry, sounding happier now the strange object had been explained. "Peter's the only person I know who can make one work."

Captain Blade's eyes brightened as he stared at the instrument in his hands. "By my beard, I do believe this is not just any old astrolabe. The gold globe . . . the bones . . ."

". . . the jewels, the symbols . . ." sighed Peter, his eyes growing wider. "Is it possible?" he breathed.

"I'd always thought it was nothing but a myth," said Blade.

"And the myth was?" asked Charlie, pulling at the captain's sleeve.

"Not a myth after all," whispered Peter, "for we have it here in our hands."

"But *what* do we have in our hands?" demanded Fernando. "Tell us!"

The two men were still staring at each other as if someone had put a spell on them.

Harry Hopp stamped his stump on the deck. "Is it what I think it is?" he demanded eagerly.

"All I can see are bones and a shiny ball," said Sam, "but you're behaving as if they were the Crown Jewels!"

"Shiver me timbers, lad, this is better than the Crown Jewels," gasped Harry Hopp. "This is the Astrolabe of Fortune!"

"We've never heard of it," Fernando burst out, looking at Sam and Charlie's puzzled faces.

"You're young and it's an ancient tale," said Captain Blade. "Hundreds of years ago, there was an old astronomer called Bartolemy.

He had amassed the most valuable
hoard of treasure you could imagine but
he had no one to leave it to, so he hid it
somewhere in the Caribbean. Then he
made the astrolabe – but he made it like
no other had ever been made before. Only
the Astrolabe of Fortune will
lead the bearer to the treasure's hiding
place."

"That's an amazing story, Captain,"
gasped Sam. He looked round at his
shipmates. "What are we waiting for?
Peter knows how to use it. We should set
sail and find the treasure."

"This is only *part* of the astrolabe," said
the captain. "When Bartolemy knew he
was dying, he separated it into four pieces.
He gave three pieces to trusted messengers
and sent them off to different points of
the compass. Not one knew where the
others were going. Then he left orders that,
after his death, this golden ball was to be

placed in his skeletal hand and buried in a secret place."

"And we've found it," breathed Ben.

"Whoever can assemble the astrolabe . . ." began Peter.

". . . and work out how to use it," Harry Hopp butted in.

"Yes, and work out how to use it," said Peter. "Well, whoever that is, he can keep the treasure." He took the globe from Captain Blade. "This is only the base. It's missing two moving pieces and the pin that holds it all together."

"Do we need those things?" asked Fernando.

Peter nodded. "Without them, this is just a pretty bauble with writing on it. Totally useless."

"So we've all got excited over nothing," said Ben. "No good talking about treasure when we've no idea where it is."

"Imagine sailing off to find the richest

haul of booty you've ever seen!" sighed
Charlie. "If only we knew where the other
pieces are."

"But we do!" shouted Sam suddenly.
"We know exactly where they are. The
treasure can be ours!"

CHAPTER FOUR

Everyone looked at him in surprise. "Don't be daft, lad," said Harry Hopp. "They could be anywhere in the world. It'll take a thousand lifetimes to find them."

"No it won't," insisted Sam. "Titus Reynard has already found them for us! Charlie said his brother was shouting about 'the last piece of the puzzle'. That must mean Reynard has got the rest of the Astrolabe of Fortune!"

"By thunder, the boy's right!" exclaimed Captain Blade.

"Well done, Sam," said Ned. "Now all we have to do is go and get those other pieces."

"It'll be a dangerous job," Peter told them. "Reynard always sets guards round his house. They'd shoot us soon as look at us."

"Belay that talk!" exclaimed the captain. "We laugh in the face of danger. It's got to be worth the risk for the promise of such riches!" He looked round at the crew, his eyes shining. "Are you all with me, my brave men?"

"Aye!" cried the pirates.

"I'll make a drawing of the missing pieces so we know what we're looking for," said Peter, his eyes shining with excitement.

"We'll pay Titus Reynard a little visit," declared Captain Blade with a smile. "But we must get there well ahead of his cowardly brother."

"If we're fast, we can be in and out before Titus even hears the news that his precious cargo has been lost," declared Fernando, looking out over the waves. "The wind's with us and we have the best ship in the Caribbean."

"We'll need it," muttered Harry as he made his way to the wheel. "The instant Reynard knows that the golden ball is in pirate hands, he'll batten down the hatches. Then we'll never get into the house."

"All hands on deck," ordered Captain Blade. "Set sail for Puerto Rico!"

The sun was low in the sky as the *Sea Wolf* sailed into a deserted bay on the eastern shore of Puerto Rico.

"Reynard's ship will scarcely have made her repairs yet," said Harry Hopp. "She'll be well behind us." He gave a loud guffaw. "Poor old Titus, little does he know he's going to have some uninvited guests."

"Who will you send into the house, Captain?" asked Fernando.

Captain Blade looked round his crew. Sam held his breath. He hoped he'd be chosen. It was going to be risky — but he didn't want to miss out on the excitement.

"Peter, you'll be one of the party, of course," said the captain at last. "You know what you're looking for."

"Aye, aye, Captain," said Peter, wiping his hands on his apron ready for the mission.

"Take Fernando with you," Blade went on. "He's a dab hand at picking locks. And you too, Charlie. You know all about grand houses as you used to live in one yourself." The pirates had rescued Charlie from her evil stepfather who had plotted to kill her to inherit all her wealth.

Sam's face fell. Was he going to be left out, after all?

"Don't look so glum, Sam." The captain patted him on the back. "You'll be going with your friends. If you can bob up to the *Sea Wolf* in a barrel without us noticing, you'll have no trouble sneaking into Reynard's house unseen."

"Thank you, Captain!" exclaimed Sam. "I won't let you down."

Peter showed Sam and his friends a piece of parchment. "I've drawn the missing parts of the astrolabe on here. Take a good look, then you'll know what we're after." He pointed to the wobbly drawing of a flat ring engraved with regular lines and numbers, a bit like a circular ruler. "This goes round the middle of the ball. And this dome thing that looks a bit like a baby's lace cap but with more holes – well, it fits over half of our ball. And here is the pin."

Sam, Charlie and Fernando studied the rough sketch. Peter seemed to be as good at drawing as he was at cooking – in other words, very bad. "Is that a hedgehog on top of the pin?" asked Sam.

"Hedgehog? No! That's a rising sun," said Peter. "Those bits poking out are the beams. Can't you see?"

"It could be a *setting* sun," said Charlie mischievously.

"No it couldn't," said Peter, sounding a bit grumpy now.

"How do you know?" asked Fernando.

"Because it's part of the story that's told," said Peter firmly. "Bartolemy made a pure gold pin in the shape of a rising sun and that's that."

"I remember that from the tale," said Captain Blade, "but the sun will definitely be setting *here* soon, so be off with you before it's too dark to see. And, remember, Reynard is a ruthless man, so take great care. If you get caught he'll swat you like flies."

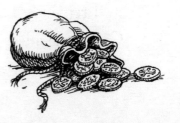

Chapter Five

The four pirates crept silently through the wooded garden of Titus Reynard's house. They'd left the *Sea Wolf* moored out of sight in a quiet bay and taken one of the rowing boats so they could slip ashore without being spotted.

Sam had to keep his excitement from bubbling over. So far everything had gone to plan. Suddenly they found themselves in full view of the huge, sprawling mansion. The sun was low behind it, throwing long shadows onto the broad carriage drive. Sam just had time to see two men with guns guarding the front door before Fernando dragged him and Charlie into the undergrowth. Peter dropped down next to them.

"We must not be seen, my friends," hissed Fernando.

They heard the sound of hooves and a coach came sweeping up the drive. A man and woman were helped out by the two men and went into the house.

"Look at their fine clothes," whispered Charlie.

"I reckon Mr Reynard's having a party," said Sam, watching two more coaches arrive. "That'll keep him busy while we search his house."

"Aye," agreed Peter. "I suggest we have some supper and then seek a way in." He pulled out four nasty-looking pies. "Who wants one?" he asked, holding them out.

Sam and the others shrank back.

"I'm still full from lunch," said Sam quickly.

"Me too," nodded Charlie.

"We can always use them to poison the guards!" Fernando whispered to Sam with a cheeky grin.

"Waste not, want not," said Peter, munching away with relish.

"It's all quiet for the moment," said Fernando. "There's just the two men at the door. I think we should take the chance while we can and slip round the back of the house."

Peter wiped the green gravy from his mouth. "There's still a pie left," he said encouragingly.

"Er, Fernando's right," Sam put in quickly. "We should go now."

Peter put the pie inside his shirt and they crept off between the trees, circling round the house to reach the back. They could see lamps being lit as the sun went down. Strains of music and laughter drifted out from inside.

"There's a window over there," hissed Sam. "We might be able to get in that way."

Keeping low, they ran to the house. Fernando peered through the glass. "No one inside."

But Sam could see the window was firmly shut.

"What are we going to do?" he asked.

"Leave it to me," said Fernando with a grin. He pulled out his knife and slid it between the frame and the window. As it reached the clasp he gave his knife a jerk. There was a soft clunk and the next moment the window swung open. Fernando pulled himself onto the sill. Charlie and Sam climbed up after him.

Peter grabbed the frame and began to haul himself up. But as he squeezed through the gap, a terrible smell rose in the air.

"I've squashed my pie," he groaned.

The three friends held their noses.

"It's an awful stench," giggled Charlie. "People will smell him all the way to Barbados!"

Peter's eyes widened in fear as an angry barking was heard in the distance.

"Guard dogs!" hissed Fernando. "They've picked up the scent."

Peter dropped to the ground. "You carry on with the mission. I'll lure the beasts away." He began to sprint towards the trees.

He had just disappeared between the tree trunks when two large dogs came bounding along. They stopped at the edge of the forest, eagerly sniffing the ground.

Sam watched through the window to make sure that their crewmate had got away.

"We'd better get searching," he heard Fernando say.

"There's no point looking in here, though," Charlie replied. "It's the laundry room. I don't think this is where the astrolabe will be hidden."

Out of the corner of his eye, Sam saw a man striding round the corner of the house — and he was carrying a rifle. Any minute now he'd discover the open window.

"Hide!" he gasped, ducking down under the sill and flattening himself against the wall.

Fernando and Charlie dived into an empty wooden washtub in the corner. Sam scarcely dared breathe as he listened to the footsteps coming closer. They stopped at the window. Now Sam could hear the

click of a trigger being set. He glanced up.
The man had stuck the barrel of his gun
through the opening and was pointing it
into the room.

CHAPTER SIX

For what seemed like hours there was silence. Finally the guard muttered something in Spanish, slammed the window shut and moved on.

"He didn't see us," reported Fernando, climbing out of the washtub.

Sam let out a ragged breath. "And luckily we didn't get squashed pie on us so he didn't smell us either!" he whispered.

"Now, what's the plan?"

"We do a bit of dressing up," replied Charlie.

The boys looked at her in horror.

"The last time you suggested that, I had to pretend to be a girl," protested Fernando. "Never again."

"We'll look too suspicious if we're found dressed like pirates," Charlie explained. "But if we wear servants' clothes no one will notice us. They'll just think we're local children, hired to work here because of the party! And don't worry, you can be a boy, Fernando."

Sam and Fernando looked round the room. No candles were lit and the light outside was fading fast.

"We're not short of servants' garb," said Fernando, pointing to a large pile of clothes lying in the corner.

Charlie began to ferret through the laundry, throwing shirts and sheets aside.

"These are too fine," she said. "They must belong to Titus or his brother . . . Wait. What's this?"

She produced plain, patched breeches and jackets. The boys pulled them on over their own clothes while Charlie climbed into a skirt and apron. She covered her hair with a white kerchief while Fernando tucked his bandana in his pocket.

Dressed in their servants' garb, they made for the door.

"Where shall we start?" said Charlie. "These astrolabe pieces are very precious to Reynard so they'll be well hidden."

"You're right," nodded Fernando. "He is a devious man. He will have devious hiding places."

"So we're looking for cupboards and hidey-holes," said Sam. "I suggest we stay together and do each room as we come to it."

"Agreed," said Charlie and Fernando.

They crept out into a corridor. Sam's stomach rumbled as he smelled roasting meat wafting from a room at the end. They could hear the bustle and clatter of a busy kitchen.

"This way," hissed Fernando, leading them in the opposite direction.

They passed a huge dining room, brightly lit with candles. Long tables were laid with plates, goblets and knives. It looked ready for a feast.

"Let's search in here before Titus and his guests come to eat," suggested Charlie. "Then while they're busy stuffing their bellies, we can have a look in the other rooms."

"Not worth it," said Sam, poking his head round the door. "There are no cupboards to hide anything in and he won't have stuffed them under the tablecloth." They moved on, searching each room, but there was no sign of the precious pieces of the astrolabe.

They came to an entrance hall. It was dark outside now and candles blazed in their sconces all around the walls. At that moment they heard loud, chattering voices approaching.

"It must be time for the feast," said Sam. "Hide."

Fernando and Charlie disappeared under

a large wooden seat and Sam dived behind a huge vase painted with dragons. Peering round, he could see a man leading the way, talking over his shoulder to his guests. He wore a rich blue coat with silver braid and shiny buttons. Rings with huge stones were crammed on every finger and a wig with long, white curls fell about his shoulders. He was smiling but Sam saw that his eyes were cold and cruel.

As soon as the crowd had passed on to the dining room they crawled out from their hiding places.

"He's a nasty-looking cove!" exclaimed Fernando. "He has a stare like an eagle."

"And a nose as sharp as a cutlass," said

Charlie with a shudder. "I remember my stepfather talking of him. Even he was scared of Reynard."

"He must be really mean if he's worse than your stepfather," said Fernando.

"Where next?" asked Sam. "Where would Reynard hide something so precious?"

Making sure there were no servants in view, Fernando led the way across the hall and tried the first door he came to. "This one's locked."

"Which means . . ." began Charlie.

". . . there could be something important in there!" finished Sam.

Fernando pulled a piece of bent metal from his belt. "It's lucky I came prepared to pick the lock," he said, feeding it carefully into the keyhole. It looked to Sam as if he was just wiggling the metal from side to side but, before long, there was a dull clunk and the door swung open.

Taking a candle from a table, Fernando crept inside with Sam and Charlie close behind. Charlie shut the door softly. It was dark because the shutters were closed and the one candle gave out a pitiful pool of light. Fernando went round the room, hurriedly lighting more candles. The only sound came from a clock that ticked quietly on the wall.

"This must be Reynard's study," whispered Sam, catching sight of a large table piled high with papers, quills and ink bottles. The walls were panelled and hung with paintings in heavy gilt frames.

Charlie stared round at the bookshelves and dark wooden furniture. "So many places to search," she murmured. "It'll take a long time."

"But the good thing is no one will disturb us," said Fernando. "Reynard's busy lording it over his guests and the servants must know he keeps this door locked. We'll have plenty of peace and quiet."

As he spoke a loud chiming filled the

air. For a second they all froze to the spot.

Then Sam managed a shaky laugh. "It's only the clock. We shouldn't worry about that making a noise. The household will be used to it."

He checked the top of the desk, looking under papers and peering into inkwells. Then he began to open the drawers.

Charlie was searching through a shelf of books, lifting each one out to see if anything was hidden behind it.

"Check inside as well," Sam urged her. "There might be a secret compartment hollowed out of the pages. I saw that at the cinema once."

"Cinema?" asked Fernando. "You do say some mad things. What is this *cinema?*"

Whoops! thought Sam. *There aren't any cinemas in 1706.* "Er . . . well . . ." he burbled. "The Cinema is the name of . . . the big house near my mum's farm. The man who lives there is always hiding things in his books." He could see Charlie trying not to laugh.

Fernando shrugged. "I'd like to see where you live one day, Sam. It sounds very strange."

You don't know how strange, my friend, thought Sam.

Fernando went round the walls, tapping the panels. "Reynard could have a secret hiding place here," he muttered.

Sam had reached the last drawer of the desk. There was no keyhole but when he pulled at the long metal handle, it wouldn't move. "This one's stiff," he groaned, tugging hard at it. "Help me, Fernando." Fernando heaved at the handle with him but the drawer wouldn't budge.

Sam looked at his friend, his eyes sparkling with excitement. "This might be where the astrolabe pieces are," he breathed. "Reynard's tried to make sure no one can find them. If only we could get it open."

"Let me see," said Charlie, bending down to look. She ran her fingers underneath the wood.

"*You* won't be able to move it if *we* can't," said Fernando.

A loud click echoed out from the desk

and the drawer sprang open. Fernando's jaw dropped in surprise.

"It was a trick," said Charlie, pulling the handle. "There's a hidden spring underneath that keeps the drawer closed until you press on it. My stepfather had a desk like this. He kept my will inside — the one he was always trying to get me to sign so he could have my money after he'd killed me."

Eagerly, the friends crowded round but, as they peered inside, Sam felt his hopes drain away like water down a plughole.

The drawer was completely empty.

CHAPTER SEVEN

"Where now?" asked Charlie, flopping into the big chair behind the desk. "We don't have long."

"I can't think where else to look!" said Sam. "Where could be safer than a secret drawer in a locked room?"

Charlie suddenly leapt to her feet. "We've been looking in the wrong places!" she exclaimed.

"We've worked that out!" said Fernando bitterly.

"No, listen," Charlie insisted. "I remember a story about Reynard being really devious. Once, he stole a very valuable diamond. Everyone suspected him but they never found it. A long time later he boasted that, instead of hiding the gem, he'd put it on view – right in the middle of his horse's bridle where no one would think to look."

"That's brilliant!" said Sam. "So Reynard might have put the astrolabe pieces on view, just like he did with the diamond."

"Exactly!" replied Charlie.

"No wonder the secret drawer was empty," said Sam. "He doesn't need it!"

"We must search again," said Fernando, "and this time among all the things on show. I'll start with the picture frames. They're so fancy that a king's jewels could be jumping out at us and we wouldn't notice!"

The clock chimed, making Sam jump.

He realised the clock was as fancy as the frames. He had to check it out. It was like the rusty old things you could see in the Backwater Bay museum at home, but this one gleamed. The metal was bright and new and the face was covered in patterns of silver leaves. Inside the circle of Roman numerals was a gold ring. It was engraved with lines and tiny numbers that made it look like a ruler. Sam's hopes came rushing back as if someone had turned a tap on. It was just like the ring that Peter had drawn.

"I've found part of the astrolabe!" he cried, climbing on a chair. "It's here on the clock."

"Well done, my friend," called Fernando, as Sam carefully removed the clock's hands and used them to lever off the gold ring.

He jumped down from the chair, threaded his neckerchief through the ring and tied it round his neck again. It hung like a huge pendant under his servant's shirt. "I reckon we've looked everywhere we can in here."

Fernando nodded. "Let's search all the other rooms again. We weren't looking for anything on display last time." He opened the door a slit. Beyond the hall, servants were bustling in and out of the dining room. "Change of plan," he reported. "There are too many people about."

"We could try upstairs," whispered Charlie.

Fernando nodded. "As soon as the hall's empty, we'll make a dash for it."

At Fernando's signal they crept back towards the entrance hall. They'd almost reached it when they heard a commotion at the front door. Sam caught sight of Charlie's startled eyes as he pushed her back into the shadows. Fernando flattened himself beside them.

"Where's Titus?" came an anxious cry and a young man burst in, closely followed by the two guards. "I must see him at once."

"Oh, no," whispered Fernando. "The brother has arrived."

"What's Reynard going to do when he finds out what happened?" Sam whispered back.

"Whatever it is, it won't make our job any easier!" muttered Charlie.

"Wilfred!" exclaimed Titus Reynard, coming into view, a glass of wine in one hand. "Where's the missing piece? Show me at once."

Wilfred gulped and stared at the floor. "It's gone," he admitted in a small voice. "We were attacked by pirates. They stole everything!"

Titus's eyes narrowed in fury and his hand clenched the glass, snapping the stem. He threw the broken pieces to the floor where they smashed into shards, the dark red wine spraying over the stones. Servants appeared at once and fell to cleaning up.

"I . . . it . . ." stammered Wilfred, turning pale. "Don't be cross with me, Titus –

there was nothing we could do, I swear. There were hundreds of them sailing under a fearsome wolf's-head flag. We fought like lions but they outgunned us."

"Such lies!" Fernando hissed in Sam's ear. "He's as slippery as his brother."

"Think of this as a delay, not a failure," Wilfred was burbling as he wiped the sweat from his forehead. "I am sure we will—"

"Enough!" snarled Titus. He glanced around to make sure they were not overheard. "I knew I shouldn't have trusted such a fool as you with the task." His eyes narrowed. "Of course, the blaggards who took it won't know what they've got. However, they'll realise it's gold and worth selling. I must go after it myself before they do. See to it that the ship's ready to sail. Where were they headed?"

Wilfred turned paler still. He backed off, his mouth opening and closing wordlessly.

"What is it now?" snapped Titus. "Speak, you snivelling worm."

His brother's voice came out as a croak. Sam craned forwards to hear the words. "I may have . . . in the heat of battle, you understand . . . I may have accidentally said something that gave away my mission to the pirates. They might have guessed that you have the rest of the astrolabe. I fear they may come for it."

For a second Titus's hand flew to his throat in shock. Then he dealt his brother a vicious blow across the face.

"You stupid dolt! If I have lost this vast fortune because of you, your life will not be worth living, brother or not! " He paced the floor, his teeth bared and his eyes blazing. "We must waste no time. The pirates will be on their way." He stopped abruptly. "Miguel, where are you?" he bellowed down a corridor.

A tall, scrawny-looking man came running and bowed respectfully.

"Double the guards and tell them to keep a close watch for pirates." Reynard barked his orders. "I know I can rely on you to do this and to ensure that my guests know nothing of the matter."

Miguel nodded.

"Any strangers found on my land are to be questioned closely," said Reynard. "I must know where my astrolabe sphere is."

"Yes sir." Miguel spun on his heel.

"Wait!" snapped Reynard. "I have one further order. When they have been 'persuaded' to talk and are of no further use . . ." a cold smile curled the corners of his thin lips, ". . . then you can slit their throats!"

CHAPTER EIGHT

Reynard swept off to join his guests with Wilfred following at his heels like a faithful dog. Miguel strode down the corridor to give his orders. The hall fell quiet as the footsteps died away.

"He won't capture us," hissed Charlie. "We're *Sea Wolf* pirates."

Sam hoped she was right. He tried not to think about having his throat slit.

They crept towards the stairs, Charlie leading the way. Sam's eyes darted about and he listened hard for anyone approaching. A door slammed and he froze to the spot. Fernando, close behind, crashed into him, sending him stumbling into Charlie in front. As she staggered across the hall, her arm caught the frame of an ornamental gong that stood on a table. Sam saw that any second now it was going to hit the wall and make a terrible din. He dived towards it and caught it just in time.

"Phew!" gasped Charlie. "If that had clanged it would have brought everyone running."

"Come on," hissed Sam. He reached the stairs and was about to go up when he realised Charlie was standing motionless, still staring at the gong.

"Wait!" Her voice sounded urgent. "Look at this." She was running her hands over a gold dome at the top of the stand.

It reminded Sam of the sieve his mum used for straining peas, but it was upside down and very intricate, with funny-shaped holes and no handle.

"It's the same shape as the one Peter drew," said Charlie in excitement. "And look, it has the same numbers and symbols on it! It must be the piece that fits over the astrolabe ball."

"Well done, Charlie!" exclaimed Fernando. "You've found the second missing piece." Charlie carefully eased the dome from the stand and slipped it into her apron pocket.

"Only the pin to go," said Sam.

"That's not going to be easy," said Charlie, frowning. "It's the smallest part."

They heard distant footsteps along the corridor.

"Someone's coming!" hissed Sam.

Fernando was already running on tiptoes up the stairs. Sam and Charlie hurried after him. They came to a landing that stretched right and left, away into the dark. Gusts of laughter reached them from the party below.

"We'll have to finish searching before anyone comes up to bed," said Charlie anxiously.

"We'll take a room each," whispered Sam. "It'll be quicker." He opened the door of a huge bedroom. Light from the burning torches in the garden flickered through the windows, making shadows move in weird shapes over the ceiling. There was just enough light to see.

Sam closed the door. *Where do I start?* he thought, wandering around and inspecting the dark ornate furniture. A large four-poster bed, draped in heavy curtains, was in the centre of the room. Beside it stood a table. On top there was a glass, a decanter of wine and a piece of wood with a long pencil-sized groove carved out of it.

In the corner he saw a tall mirror, the glass and rich decoration round its frame catching the light from the torches outside. Sam inspected the frame but there was no sign of the pin.

Then he noticed a chest of drawers in the darkest corner. There was a small box on it, similar to the one his mum kept her jewellery in. He lifted the lid. He could feel that the box was full of rings. "A great place to hide a

pin!" he muttered to himself, his hopes rising as he ferreted through the contents.

He nearly jumped out of his skin when he heard voices close by.

"Look after our guests, Wilfred. I will retire to my chamber."

It was Reynard and he was just outside! Sam held his breath, hoping this wasn't his bedroom.

But, to his horror, the door began to open. There was only one thing to do. He threw himself under the bed.

He heard Wilfred's pleading voice at the door.

"I'll hear no more," Reynard shouted back. "I am sick to my stomach with the trouble you've caused, brother, and I am in no mood for jollity. Miguel will wake me if any pirates are found."

"But Titus," Wilfred sounded desperate, "don't leave me alone with your guests. I never know what to say—"

"Be quiet!" hissed Reynard angrily. "I don't want to see your face until tomorrow, unless you can show me the stolen base of my astrolabe. Go and play the host. Surely even you can't get that wrong. And send me up a servant."

The door slammed. Sam held his breath as he heard footsteps moving about the room. He peeped out from under the overhanging counterpane. Reynard was striding towards him, a candle lighting up his angry face. Had he been spotted? Sam kept very still. He heard Reynard slam the candlestick onto the bedside table,

his feet only centimetres from Sam's
nose.

There was a timid knock on the door
and a man entered and came into Sam's
view. "You called for me, sir?" he said
nervously.

"Why are you dithering about, man?"
snapped Reynard. "Get these clothes off
me."

Reynard threw himself into a chair.
He made no attempt to help, but just
stuck out his hands for his rings to be
removed. Then, with trembling fingers, the
servant tried to undo the white cravat at
his neck.

"Mind what you're doing," snarled

Reynard, viciously slapping the man's hand away. "You're pinching my skin." He removed something from his cravat and held it out. The servant took it and scurried towards the jewellery box that Sam had searched.

Will he see that someone's been poking about in there? thought Sam anxiously.

At that moment, Reynard gave an angry shout. "No! That does not go in the box. By my bed, you brainless idiot. I must keep it close to me."

Sam watched intently as the servant scampered over to the table and placed the object on the small wooden stand. *What is it that Reynard is so keen to keep beside him?* Sam wondered. *Could it be what we're looking for?*

As soon as the villain was asleep, Sam would take a look!

The trembling servant returned to Reynard, carrying a long white nightshirt.

He helped him out of his clothes and made him ready for bed.

Then he began to close the shutters. "Leave them open!" snapped his master. "You know I like to be woken by the sun."

The servant scurried out and Reynard climbed into bed. He snuffed the candle so that only the lights from the garden lit the shadows. Sam listened intently. The man was restless, tossing and turning, muttering angrily to himself. Sam ached to move but he knew only too well what would happen if he was caught. Then he remembered Charlie and Fernando. They were sure to come looking for him soon. They might be captured too!

Long minutes passed. Finally Reynard's breathing changed. He began to snore. Sam eased himself out from under the bed. For a moment he stood gazing at Reynard – an ugly sight, lying on his back,

great rumbling snorts coming out of his
open mouth. As long as Sam made no
noise, he was sure he was safe.

He bent over the bedside table. It was
in deep shadow and at first he couldn't
see anything. Scarcely daring to breathe,
he felt for the wooden stand, but his hand
knocked into the candlestick and it scraped
along the table. The noise sounded
deafening to Sam and at once Reynard
stirred. Sam's heart thumped so hard
against his ribs he was sure it was going to
burst out of his chest, but then Reynard
muttered something in his sleep and began
to snore again.

Slowly and silently, Sam's fingertips moved along the table until they touched the wooden stand. Something long and thin was lying in the groove. Trembling with excitement, he picked it up and held it to the window. Now he could clearly see it, silhouetted against the glow from outside. It was a metal pin and at one end was a small semicircle with rays spreading out from it.

Sam knew what he was holding. It was the astrolabe pin with the rising sun. The last missing part of the Astrolabe of Fortune! No wonder Reynard had worn it and kept it close to him even while he slept. And Sam remembered his hand flying to cover it when his brother had told him the bad news of the pirates' raid.

Now they could set off to get the treasure. Sam just managed to stop himself from whooping with excitement.

He fixed the pin inside his borrowed shirt and tiptoed for the door. His hand was just reaching for the handle when there was an angry cry behind him. Sam gasped and spun round.

Titus Reynard was awake.

CHAPTER NINE

For a split second Reynard gawped at him. "Thief!" he croaked.

Sam knew that if he tried to run now, Reynard would raise the alarm. Somehow he had to persuade him that he wasn't a thief caught red-handed in his bedroom. But how? He couldn't pretend he was there to mend the plumbing. Then he had an idea.

He solemnly held up a hand. "Titus," he intoned in the spookiest voice he could manage.

Reynard shut his mouth in surprise.

"You are a bad man," Sam continued in an eerie whisper. "I am the ghost of . . . Billy, the servant boy that you whipped so cruelly. I died of my wounds." Sam thought it was a safe bet that Reynard had whipped at least one of his servants to death.

"Billy? What? Who?" gabbled the villain, plucking at his bedcovers in horror.

"You can't have forgotten me," wailed Sam. "I swore that I would come back and haunt you for your evil deed — and here I am!"

Reynard groaned and hid under the sheet.

Sam was about to creep out of the door when

Reynard's head reappeared. "Begone, you foul fiend," he whimpered.

Sam waved a warning finger. "Make no mistake, Titus Reynard. I will be back. I will haunt you until you change your wicked ways."

The sheet dropped from Reynard's shaking fingers. He scrabbled to pull it up again, terror written all over his face. Sam made a low moaning cry, just like he'd seen ghosts do on television, and felt for the doorknob. Keeping his eyes on Reynard and groaning away, he opened the door a crack and began to slip through.

"Wait a minute!" The man's voice was suddenly harsh. "Ghosts don't use doors! They go through walls. You're no more a phantom than I am."

His hand flew to the empty wooden holder and he gave a cry. "You've taken my pin!" The next second he was fighting free of his sheets.

Sam was out and had the door slammed shut in an instant. He ran along the landing, making for the stairs. Behind him, Reynard was bellowing from inside his bedroom.

"Help! Pirate thief!"

Now footsteps were coming up towards him from the hall. Sam froze, wondering what to do next. Suddenly a hand shot out from an open doorway and pulled him inside. As the door closed behind him he made out the two shadowy figures of his friends. He slumped against the wooden panels in relief.

"Where were you?" hissed Fernando. "Charlie and I have been waiting an age!"

"I've got the pin!" said Sam.

"Well done!" exclaimed Charlie. "We have everything we came for."

"There's one little problem," said Sam. "I got it from Reynard's bedside — and he saw me take it!"

Charlie gasped.

At that moment, they heard feet thundering along the landing and Reynard's furious voice as he ran down the stairs shouting at everybody.

"They're after you, my friend," whispered Fernando. "How do we escape?"

Charlie looked through the window. "We can't risk climbing down that way," she said grimly. "There's a long drop and there could still be guards in the grounds."

"We can't stroll out of the door either," said Fernando. "They'll catch us straight away!"

"No they won't!" said Sam eagerly. He'd had a brilliant idea. Well, he hoped it was brilliant. They didn't have any other choice. "Reynard couldn't see my face in the dark. If we mingle with the others we won't stand out. We're dressed as servants, after all."

Charlie chuckled. "Clever plan! We're doing what Reynard did with the pieces of the astrolabe. We'll be on view but no one will know who we are!"

Fernando opened the door a crack. "There are plenty of servants sniffing around. Good time to make for the stairs!"

Heads down, the three friends slipped out amongst the crowd and ran along the landing, trying to look as if they were on the trail of the pirate thief. Sam went cold as he heard Reynard's voice barking angry instructions amid the puzzled questions of his guests, yet, each time he dared to glance up, he could see that no one was

paying any attention to the three extra youngsters in servants' clothes. A few more minutes and they'd be out of the house and away to their ship.

But as they reached the top of the staircase they heard Reynard shrieking from his study. "That thief has got everything. He has to be stopped. You, there! Don't stand around – get yourselves upstairs and search everyone you find. And I mean *everyone!*"

A jostling group of men appeared at the foot of the stairs. They were brandishing sharp knives. It was too late to escape and Sam knew there was no time to get their finds to a safe place before they were searched. But Fernando was rummaging in his servant's breeches. Sam saw him drop something over the banister. As the men began to climb, a loud clang sounded from the gong in the hallway. They stopped and turned back, knives at the ready.

"Follow me!" Fernando hissed to the others.

"That was quick thinking," Sam muttered as they raced through the nearest door to get out of sight.

Fernando pulled a mock sad face. "I found a nice bit of cheese left out for the guests. I have sacrificed our hungry bellies to save our lives."

"And I'm glad you did," said Sam. "Although I'm so hungry I could even eat one of Peter's pies. What shall we do now? We can't go back out there."

They were standing in a small room stacked with travelling chests.

"I looked round this room earlier," said Charlie. "There's a veranda roof outside. We might be able to escape from here without being seen."

"It's our only chance," agreed Sam. "Let's go!"

Once out on the sloping veranda roof, it

was a small drop down onto the drive at the front. They crouched low as they heard the shouts of men searching in the distance.

"We can't go back to the ship the way we came," said Charlie in a low voice. "There are too many torches. We'll be seen."

"This way," said Fernando, creeping round the corner of the house where low bushes were growing in rows. "We can use these as cover."

They moved between the rows in a stooping run.

"What's that minty smell?" asked Sam. "It's like bubblegum."

"Bubblegum?" hissed Fernando. "Is that some horrible disease you get in your mouth?"

Whoops! thought Sam. *Fernando won't have heard of bubblegum.*

"We're in a herb garden, Sam," said Charlie. "That's peppermint you can smell."

"Of course," said Sam quickly. "Peppermint always makes my gums bubble."

"You are strange, my friend," muttered Fernando as he pushed through the bushes.

"We're nearly at the trees," panted Charlie at last. "We've escaped."

"Oi!" A bellow split the air. "Stop right there!"

CHAPTER TEN

Sam, Charlie and Fernando froze as three burly men came running up, guns in their hands.

"Who's there?" snarled one. "I don't recognise any of you."

"Nor do I." The man next to him had a nasty grin on his face. "But Mr Reynard said the pirate thief was a boy, and these look just the right age. I reckon it's one of you two lads."

"Leave this to me!" whispered Charlie.

Before the boys could stop her, she'd fallen to her knees. "Oh, help us, kind sirs," she wailed. She'd changed her voice to sound like a servant and let out a torrent of words. "My mistress is poorly. Her ladyship's stomach is that upset after the fine feast and all this noise and shouting and she said we had to pick her some peppermint from the garden or she'd never be well again and I was too scared to come out on my own because of the wicked pirate thief so these two grooms came with me and . . ." She broke off, her eyes full of terror ". . . and suddenly we were nearly bowled over by a bunch of vicious pirates!"

"That's right, sirs," added Fernando, keeping his head bent. "We feared for our lives and hid in these bushes."

Sam saw his chance to help out. "They went that way." He pointed back to the house, in the opposite direction to their escape route.

"Sounds like the pirate boy has got accomplices," said the first man, setting off for the house. "We'll have to release the dogs again."

The minute the men were out of sight, Sam and his friends sprinted for the trees and made for the shore without stopping.

"Where's Peter?" said Fernando anxiously. "There's the boat, hidden behind the rocks where we left it, so he can't have gone back to the *Sea Wolf*."

"Ahoy, shipmates!" came a hoarse cry above their heads. "Any sign of those dogs?"

They looked up. Peter's frightened face was peering down at them from a coconut palm.

"It's all clear," Sam reassured him. "You can come down. Mission accomplished."

Still smelling strongly of pie, Peter clambered to the ground, trying to pull his shirt down to cover a huge fang-shaped hole in his trousers. Shedding their disguises, the three friends dragged the boat down to the water. Fernando seized the oars and rowed hard for the *Sea Wolf*. Sam kept his eyes fixed on the land to make sure that no one was following.

At last the wooden hull of their ship loomed over them. Sam leapt on to the deck, with Fernando, Charlie and Peter close behind.

Sinbad streaked out of the hold and into Charlie's arms, purring loudly.

"We've got everything we need for the astrolabe!" panted Fernando, as they triumphantly held up their finds for the crew to see.

"And we have to set sail straight away!" declared Sam.

"Hold hard!" laughed Captain Blade.

"You young 'uns have done a magnificent job – but I usually give the orders, Sam. Why the hurry?" He scanned the shore with his spyglass. "No one followed you."

"But Reynard knows we've taken all the pieces," said Sam. "When we escaped he was still searching the house, but once he realises we've got away he'll come after us."

Blade nodded. "Good thinking, lad. We'll get right away from here while we're working out the route to the treasure."

"Pieces of eight!" squawked Crow, landing on Sam's head.

"I'm glad you're back, lad," said Ned. "I've had a deal of trouble keeping this bird from following you."

Eyes shining, Peter fixed the astrolabe together, securing it with the pin. He held the completed instrument up for everyone to see.

The dome from the gong fitted perfectly around half the golden ball, showing the

jewelled surface beneath. The disc
from the clock was held firmly
in place by the pin.

*It looks a bit like Saturn lying
on its side,* thought Sam. But he
remembered to keep it in his head. He
had no idea if the pirates had heard of the
planet with its mysterious rings.

"I've found a couple of words here,"
Peter was saying. "I think they might be
important. Only I'm not too good with
my letters . . ."

Sam knew that most of the pirates
couldn't read or write. "I'll have a look!"
he said eagerly, squinting at the tiny words
on the edge of the ring. "Is-o-la Monica!"
he read slowly. "What does that mean?"

"It means we know where to find the
treasure!" declared Peter. "Isola Monica is
a tiny island six hours from here."

"It's not much more than a rock with
a few ruins," sniffed Harry. "There's

nowhere to hide treasure there. It's a wild goose chase, I say."

"If that's what's written on the astrolabe, then that's where we're going," said the captain. "Look lively, men. It's full sail north-west. There's a fair chance that Reynard will have read those words too. He'll know about Isola Monica and, once he's sure the thief has escaped, he'll be bound to head there."

"Then let's hope he's searching his house for a good time yet," called Fernando as he made for the rigging. "By the time he arrives we'll have found the treasure and gone."

"Aye and, as luck would have it, Isola Monica is not far from Skeleton Island," said Ben.

"By Orion's belt," chuckled Captain Blade, "we'll soon be sitting safe in that stronghold and counting our booty."

Peter was carefully turning the gold ring around the sphere.

"Have you worked out what it all means?" asked Sam.

Peter shook his head. "Not yet," he said. "I know it's the key to the treasure but I don't know how. It's strange. There are symbols of the rising sun all over it — that must be important. And look here." He held the astrolabe up to his eye. "Bartolemy has bored tiny holes here. I can see right through it. I wonder why he did that." He turned it over in his hands. "But it won't defeat me. I'll work it out or I'll eat my ladle!"

"Be careful what you promise," laughed Harry Hopp from the wheel.

"It would taste better than his cooking!" Charlie whispered to Sam.

The faint glow of dawn was beginning to show on the horizon as a tiny rocky island came into view. Through his spyglass Sam

could make out a tall tower and the ruins of an old fortress. To stern, the sea was empty. Reynard had not caught up with them yet.

"There's our anchorage," said Blade, pointing to a deep inlet. "The *Sea Wolf* won't easily be spotted if she's hidden by those cliffs."

Peter came out of the galley, carrying the astrolabe. He looked worried. "Captain, I still cannot fathom how this works," he said, frowning. "I've set it by the present position of the stars, just like you'd do with any other astrolabe, but no matter how I twist it and turn it, it's telling me nothing. All we know from the story is that sunrise is important."

"And sunrise is not far off," said Blade. "Get aboard the boat with the landing party, Peter. With luck, it will all become clear when we arrive on the island."

Sam and Fernando rowed through the

dark water while Charlie sat between Ned and Harry Hopp at the stern. Captain Blade and Peter were at the bow. Only the sound of the oars and Peter's anxious muttering broke the silence as they neared the shore.

Soon they were tying up the boat and eyeing the steep slope to the fortress.

"There's nothing here but those ruins," said Ned, holding up a lantern.

"And bare rock," said Charlie.

Blade nodded. "It would be impossible to bury the treasure, so it must be hidden somewhere in the stones of the fort. Have you found out anything more, Peter?"

Peter was staring gloomily at the instrument. He shook his head.

"Well, it's a place to start our search at least," said Ned, setting off towards the ruins.

They clambered over the low crumbling walls to stand in the remains of the fortress.

The walls made a square around them with the tower on the western side.

A low stone column stood on its own in the centre of the square.

"Well, I'll jump over Jamaica!" exclaimed Ned, nudging a broken pickaxe with his toe. "Someone's been trying to dig the rock up at the base of this funny round pillar thing."

"Reynard!" Harry Hopp spat out the

name. "I bet it was him – or, rather, his servants."

"You were right, Captain Blade," said Sam. "He must have seen the name of the island too."

"It didn't do him any good though, did it?" said Ned cheerfully.

"But now we *know* he'll be on his way again," said Charlie. "We need to find the treasure and be off before he arrives."

Sam was staring intently at the column. "There are some marks here," he said, running his fingers round the sides. "They're just like the rising sun symbols on the astrolabe."

"No wonder Reynard tried to dig here," said Fernando.

Sam gave a gasp. "And look! There's a hollow in the top – and a deep groove. I think I know just what that's for!" He took the astrolabe from Peter's hands and gently lowered it into the hollow.

"By Jupiter, it's a perfect fit!" cried Captain Blade as the gold ring slipped into the groove.

"But what now?" asked Fernando impatiently. "It's still not telling us anything."

"I reckon we have to wait," said Sam in excitement. "And I don't think it will be long."

Peter's face lit up in a slow grin. "You mean we wait for the *sunrise*," he declared. "Of course!"

Everyone stared intently at the golden orb. Behind the ruins of the eastern wall, the sun was slowly creeping over the island. But nothing was happening to the Astrolabe of Fortune. The *Sea Wolf* pirates looked at each other in dismay.

"It's not working," whispered Charlie.

CHAPTER ELEVEN

Suddenly a ray of sun shone through a tiny gap in the wall and hit the astrolabe. The artefact glowed as if it was alive.

Sam shouted in triumph and the crew followed his pointing finger towards the top of the tower. A bright circle of light was shining on the crumbling old stones just under the roof.

"That's where the treasure will be!" shouted Ned. "In the bell tower. The astrolabe has shown us. It must be magic!"

Sam knew what had happened. Bartolemy had set the whole thing up. When the clever old astronomer made his special astrolabe he must have put mirrors inside it. If the astrolabe was adjusted to the right star setting and placed on the column he'd built, then, when the sun shone through the wall and into one of the holes in the instrument, the mirrors reflected the light onto the tower. Sam didn't say anything – magic was much more fun!

"It's the Astrolabe of *Good* Fortune," said

Fernando, a huge grin on his face.

As quickly as it had come, the light had gone from the wall of the tower but that didn't matter. Everyone knew where to look now.

They ran to the doorway of the old ruin. Captain Blade stepped inside, glanced towards the roof and came out shaking his head. "I can't see anywhere for treasure to be hidden," he said. "There's just an ancient staircase in there."

"And those stairs don't look like they'll last much longer," said Harry.

"But that's where the astrolabe is telling us to search!" insisted Sam. "I'll go. I'm not too heavy."

He began to climb the crumbling steps that wound up inside the tower. It was dark except for a narrow slit of light near the top. He thought he could make out the shape of an old bell up there. He forced himself not to look down at the distant floor but to keep his eyes on the narrow stairs.

He slipped as his foot caught a loose stone. It fell, crashing loudly against the steps. Sam clung to the wall, his stomach churning with fear.

"Are you all right?" came Blade's anxious voice.

"Aye, Captain," called Sam, trying to sound calm. "Nearly there."

At last he found himself at the top, level with the huge bell. It was tied to the single rafter in the roof by a frayed rope. The rope didn't seem strong enough to be holding such a heavy weight. Sam peered through the small slit in the wall. He could just make out the astrolabe glowing on its column.

"I reckon I've reached the spot where the light hit," he muttered to himself. He inspected the stones all around. They were smooth, with no ledges or hiding places where treasure could be stashed. Sam began to wonder if they'd been tricked. Was the old astronomer having the last laugh? Or had someone stumbled upon the treasure years ago?

"There's no sign of anything hidden here," he called down. "The only place big enough for treasure is the bell and it can't be in there!" He drew out his cutlass and pushed it up into the bell to prove it. To his astonishment, the cutlass point had hardly passed the rim when it knocked against something. Sam tried again. There was definitely something blocking the bell. His heart beating fast, Sam leaned out over the drop and peered up into the dome. It was hard to see in the dim light of the tower but, instead of a huge hollow void, it looked as if the bell had been completely stoppered up with a round sheet of metal. He gave the bell a push, and heard a faint rattling inside. *That doesn't sound like a bell clapper,* he thought in excitement. *That sounds like treasure!*

"I think I've found it!" he cried out loud.

There was a great cheer from his friends waiting below and when Sam dared to look down he saw Fernando's grinning face appear at the bottom of the tower.

"Well done, my friend!" Fernando called. "Send it this way. We'll catch it." Charlie joined him and the two of them held out what looked like Peter's long shirt.

Sam put the point of his sword gently between the wall of the bell and the metal stopper to try to ease it out but, with a sharp scraping sound, the stopper suddenly swung down on a hinge.

"Look out below!" cried Sam. Necklaces and brooches, jewelled cups and gold coins showered out, flashing past Sam's astonished eyes and tumbling down the tower towards his friends.

"I didn't mean all at once!" Fernando shouted up when the cascade had finally stopped.

"A magnificent haul!" came Captain Blade's delighted voice. "Now we must be off before Reynard shows his ugly face."

A strange creaking noise made Sam look up in alarm. The fibres of the rope holding the bell were breaking! As he watched, another snapped, then another. The creaking grew louder and suddenly the bell was swinging wildly, its rusty clapper banging against its sides.

"Watch out below!" he cried.

Charlie and Fernando looked up in horror. They had only just dragged the treasure out of the tower when the rope snapped. Sam flattened himself to the wall as the bell dropped, crashing against the steps and sending shards of stone into the air. Finally it hit the ground and lay still.

"Sam!" It was Charlie. "You've got to get out now!"

"I'm coming," said Sam shakily.

"Hurry!" yelled Fernando. "The tower's crumbling!"

Fernando was right. Sam realised that
stones were tumbling down all around
him. He almost lost his balance as he felt
the tower shudder. The air was full of

dust. Coughing and spluttering, he began
to inch his way blindly down the steps. He
couldn't tell how far he'd gone. The tower
was trembling as if it was being shaken by
a massive earthquake. Sam clung to the
wall, put out a foot and felt – nothing.
The steps below had gone! He was
trapped.

Chapter Twelve

"Jump!" He heard Ned's voice yelling at him.

Sam froze. How could he jump? He couldn't see a thing but he knew he was still too high. He could be plummeting to his death.

"Trust Ned!" yelled Charlie. "It's your only chance."

And Sam knew he had to do just that.

He took a deep breath and launched himself blindly into the air. The next second he felt himself caught by two strong arms and Ned was running with him. There was a deafening boom and they both tumbled to the ground.

Sam sat up and wiped the grit from his eyes. Ned was sprawled beside him. All around, the crew were dusting their clothes down and coughing in the gritty air.

"Thanks, Ned," gasped Sam. He looked back at the ruins of the tower. "You saved me. I'd have been flattened."

Ned grinned.

"Well, Sam, I reckon you can thank the Astrolabe of Fortune as well," panted Harry Hopp. "It brought *you* good fortune."

"But Sam was nearly squashed," laughed Charlie. "That's not good fortune."

"Aye, but he wasn't," said Harry, his eyes twinkling. "If it had brought *bad* fortune, he'd still have been inside."

They made their way over the rocky terrain to the boats. Spirits high, Peter began a shanty as they rowed back to the *Sea Wolf*.

"Set sail for Skeleton Island," cried the captain, striding to the wheel. "We've got the best haul in the Caribbean, thanks to Peter and our brave youngsters. I've never seen such riches but I won't be happy until we've got them stowed in our stronghold. Everyone, to your posts!"

Sam scampered up the rigging to the crow's nest.

"Ahoy, me hearty," squawked his parrot friend, flapping down from the top of the mast.

"Hello, Crow," said Sam, stroking his feathered head. "This adventure is over and I'll be going back home to the future at any moment."

"Back home to the future!" shrieked Crow.

 "Shhhh!" said Sam. "Someone might hear you."

While Crow sat on his shoulder and nibbled his ear, Sam waited for the familiar tingling in his fingers and toes that meant the coin was going to whisk him back to his bedroom. It didn't come. And then as they cleared the island, he saw why. A huge ship was bearing down on them. Three rows of cannon could be seen at the gun ports. The adventure wasn't over yet.

"Ship ahoy!" he called down to the captain. "On the starboard side."

He focused his spyglass on the painted name on the prow – *Master of the Ocean*. He turned his attention to the figure on the distant poop deck. He'd recognise that cruel, haughty face anywhere.

"It's Reynard!" he yelled.

"Scurvy knave!" squawked Crow.

"You're right," agreed Sam. "He must have been lying in wait for us while we were on Isola Monica."

BOOM! The enemy cannon roared and the *Sea Wolf* rocked as the balls crashed into the water a few yards from the hull.

"What are your orders, Captain?" Sam heard Harry shout. "Do we fight back?"

"No," Blade called back. "We've got the booty and they want it. They'll not try to sink us and risk losing it. I'll warrant they'll want to board us, so let's not give them the chance. If we get to Skeleton Island before they do, we'll be safe."

Sam knew this was true. It sounded mad to lead an enemy straight to your stronghold, but only the men of the *Sea Wolf* could navigate the wild sea and dangerous rocks around Skeleton Island. Only the men of the *Sea Wolf* could find the hidden gap and sail into the calm bay

beyond. Any enemy following the ship would see her disappear and think she must have been wrecked.

"Aye, aye, Captain," said Harry, stomping across the deck. "Hoist the topsails," he bellowed to the crew.

Fernando came scrambling up the rigging towards Sam to carry out the order. He edged out over the yard below the crow's nest, releasing the ties. At once the sails swelled with wind and Sam felt the *Sea Wolf* surge forwards.

"We can outrun them now, my friend," panted Fernando, holding the edge of Sam's basket to catch his breath.

Sam looked back at the *Master of the Ocean*. The distance between them was growing but he could see men climbing her rigging. "I hope you're right," he told Fernando. "Reynard's doing the same as us. He's under full sail too – and he has more of them!"

The *Sea Wolf* sped across the waves, making for Skeleton Island and safety. At last Sam could see their hideout looming, the towering rocks making dark silhouettes against the sky.

But their enemy was closing in on them. Sam heard a voice calling across the water.

"Give up now, Blade." It was Titus. Sam looked through his spyglass at him. The villain was standing on the foredeck, his hands cupped round his mouth. "There is nowhere for you to run. You are too near the vicious rocks. Give me the treasure and I'll spare your lives."

"Thank you for the kind offer," Blade called back. "But we will have to decline."

At once Sam heard the thump of the enemy's cannon and more balls came whistling over the water.

"Keep a straight course!" bellowed Captain Blade.

Sam looked back. The *Master of the Ocean* was turning to fire again. He counted thirty gun ports, all with black cannon pointing right at them.

He gulped. He felt hot and cold at the same time. The villains had more guns and a bigger vessel. Was Reynard going to blast them out of the sea, after all? He remembered the horror of his nightmare – the *Sea Wolf* smashed in two and sinking below the waves. Was it going to come true?

CHAPTER THIRTEEN

BOOM! The blast from the enemy cannon rocked the *Sea Wolf*.

"Sam," Captain Blade's voice could be heard above the sound of firing, "we're relying on you to guide us through."

"Aye, aye, Captain!" Sam shouted back. He fixed his eyes on the rocks directly in front of them. The crew were making sure that the ship was heading straight for the highest rock, the one in the shape of a shark's fin. Sam knew that it was up to him, the lookout boy, to get the *Sea Wolf* through the hidden gap in the rocks. He was the only one high enough to see the exact place for her to turn into the bay and avoid certain death. But the sea was churning, the ship was lurching dangerously from side to side and the enemy was right on their tail. Could he do it?

The cannon fire stopped for a moment and Sam heard a bellow from the *Master of the Ocean*. It was Reynard and he sounded furious. "They're going to wreck their own vessel on that rock!" Sam caught his words above the raging sea. "Board them as soon as we're close enough. I'm not losing my treasure to the ocean!"

Sam knew he mustn't turn from his task but he was desperate to see how close the *Master of the Ocean* had come. It sounded as if Reynard's men would be boarding at any moment.

"Where's the gap?" he muttered to himself, his eyes flitting over the solid wall of Shark Fin Rock dead ahead. Then he saw a sliver of daylight. It was the hidden channel coming into view. Only those who dared sail this close would ever see it.

"To starboard!" he yelled at the top of his voice. The sails snapped round and the *Sea Wolf* lurched, almost throwing Sam out of the crow's nest.

"I don't care how near the rocks we are," Reynard was screaming at his crew. "I want my treasure, you lazy good-for-nothings!"

As Sam clung to the basket he heard his captain's voice. "I am sorry to disappoint you, Reynard, but the riches are going down to Davy Jones' Locker with us." Sam saw Blade giving his enemy a

sweeping bow. "It will be a quick death.
Farewell!"

With that, the *Sea Wolf* slipped out of
the enemy's sight.

Sam and the crew sat by a roaring fire outside the strong wooden walls of their stockade. They'd all helped to cook a splendid meal of freshly caught fish and now they were gazing longingly at their glittering treasure. No one dared touch it. Sinbad was curled up in the middle of the haul, swiping at anyone whose hand came near.

"That old astronomer missed a trick," said Ben sourly, rubbing a scratch on his arm. "He didn't need to scatter his astrolabe all over the world. He just needed one of Sinbad's ancestors to guard it."

"But then no one would have found it," laughed Captain Blade.

"Apart from me," cooed Charlie, scooping him up and rubbing her face on his tummy. Sinbad purred loudly and rolled in her arms like a kitten.

The rest of the crew dived in and began to examine their booty.

"Shiver me timbers!" exclaimed Harry Hopp, holding up a diamond necklace. "I'll warrant we'll not see such a fine haul for many a day."

"That won't stop us searching for more though," said Ben with a grin. "There's nothing better than finding a stash of riches."

"And spending it!" Ned gave a huge chuckle.

"What are we going to do with the astrolabe," asked Sam, "now that it's done its job?"

Captain Blade stroked his beard. "Well, it's made of gold so that makes it valuable—"

"We shouldn't risk doing anything further with it," interrupted Harry Hopp firmly. "It brought us good fortune and that's where it should end."

"I agree," said Peter. "I say we bury it

here and leave it in peace."

Charlie nodded. "That way it'll always bring luck to Skeleton Island."

"Aye," cried the crew.

"Then it's decided," said the captain. "Peter, fetch a spade. You can have the honour of laying it to rest."

Sam watched Peter digging a deep hole, while the rest of the crew stood round swigging their rum.

As Peter placed the golden instrument back into Bartolemy's skeletal hand and lowered it gently into the hole, the crew gave a rousing cheer.

"Shiver me timbers!" cried Harry happily. "No one will ever find it there."

Sam looked round at their smiling faces and then at the *Sea Wolf* anchored in the calm bay.

I love being a pirate, he thought.

A strong tingling sensation crept into his fingers and toes. It was time to head off to the future. Now the astrolabe was safely buried, the adventure really was over. But Sam couldn't just disappear in front of everyone.

"I've got to go," he whispered to Charlie.

She nodded. "Don't worry," she told him. "I'll say you had to get back to your mum. See you soon."

Sam threw himself behind the stockade. He'd just made it when he was sucked up into a dark swirling rush of air and, in the next instant, he found himself sprawled on his bedroom carpet.

There was a knock at his door. Sam scrambled to his feet just as his mum poked her head in.

"You're up and dressed early," she said in surprise. "Ready for some breakfast?"

"Yes please." He couldn't tell her that he'd just had a magnificent feast on a sunny beach, back in 1706. Anyway, he could always manage some toast.

He joined his dad, who was at the kitchen table watching the television.

"Look at this," said his father. "Archaeologists have found something really valuable, buried on a tiny island in the Caribbean, and no one knows how it got there."

"What do you mean, Dad?" asked Sam.

"Well, it was put there hundreds of years ago," answered Dad, "but the reporter has just said that the island's totally inaccessible except by helicopter."

"And there weren't any helicopters then," added Mum.

"You're right," said Dad. "It's a complete mystery."

Sam saw a reporter walking along a sandy beach. He sat absolutely still as he recognised the bay and the jagged rocks around Skeleton Island. "They must have found the Astrolabe of Fortune!" he gasped.

"... and here is the fabulous Astrolabe of Fortune," said the reporter, holding out the golden instrument in its skeletal hand to the camera.

"How did you know that?" asked Sam's mum in astonishment.

"Er, I must have heard it ..." Sam's brain whirred for an answer. "I must have heard it on the radio," he went on. "I couldn't sleep so I was listening to it earlier."

The reporter was still talking. "Everyone agrees that this is a very important find. And one thing's for certain, we may never know how such an incredible artefact ended up here on this inaccessible rock."

Sam grinned to himself. He knew exactly how the astrolabe had ended up on Skeleton Island, but he wasn't going to tell anyone. That was all part of being an undercover pirate. You had to know when to keep a secret!

The Sea Wolf

Charlie Fleetwood
Deckhand

Ben Hudson
Quartermaster

Sam Silver
Lookout

Ned Wainwright
Bosun

Harry Hopp
First Mate